Ghostly

Compiled by D

Longman

Contents

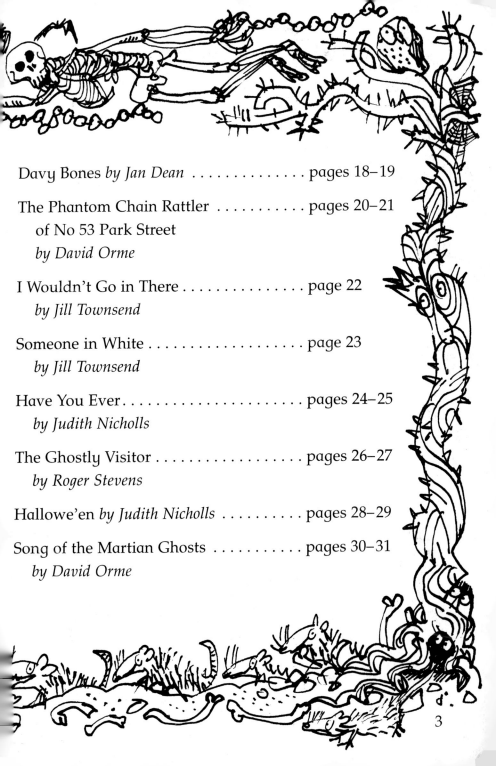

A Few Bathroom Beasts

I'm the gurgly ghost behind the sink.
When you turn on the tap
For a midnight drink
The bathroom mirror will give you a wink.
And when I'm in the mood to tease
I'll reach through the tiles
And tickle your knees!

I'm the spider lurking down the plug
With hairy legs and an ugly mug,
And a mouth full of teeth set out in rows;
When you're in your bath
I'll bite your toes!

I'm the green-eyed monster in the loo.
When it's dark at night,
I'll come for you,
I'll grab your bottom
And pull you down,
And in the drain
I'll let you drown.

David Orme

Scared

I'm scared of the night
said the nervous spook
I don't like the owls
when they hoot, hoot, hoot.

I'm scared of the dark
when the moon's not bright
I don't like the trees
when they're out of sight.

I'm scared all the time
I want to be brave
cried the nervous spook
by a cold, dark grave.

Moira Clark

What I Find Scary

What I find scary are things that go

BUMP slither Splat! THUD creeeeeeeeeeeeeeeeeeeak tt ttt ttttt tttt hooooooo OO o ooooooo

in the night

Roger Stevens and Michael Leigh

I Don't Believe in People

"I don't believe in people,"
The ghost in armour said,
"There's no such thing as a creature
That walks before it's dead!

"My friend the headless coachman
Says he saw a person one night,
He was really cross when I told him
It was just a trick of the light.

"He was driving his coach in the moonlight,
When a person-like figure appeared;
It ran off and jumped in the bushes,
With a scream that was horribly weird.

"And Magnus the Monk says he saw one;
He was having a haunt on his own,
When a creature turned up wearing very odd clothes,
And fell to the ground with a groan.

"Maybe they come in the daytime,
As I sleep in my dungeon cell,
But I'm scared to go out by myself in the light
So there's really no way I can tell.

"I don't think I believe in people,
But there's one thing that worries me,
Things get moved when I'm not around –
Now how can that possibly be?"

David Orme

Spooked

When your house feels strange
but you can't say why,
When you wake at night
to the echo of a cry,

When the floorboards creak
to the faintest footfall
and the temperature drops
for no reason at all …

You've been spooked by a spook,
now you're host to a ghost.

SQUEAK

CREAK

When the rocking chair rocks
but there's no one there,
When something has triggered
your squeaky stair,

When the curtains move
but there isn't a breeze.
When the house is empty
but you hear a sneeze …

You've been spooked by a spook,
now you're host to a ghost.

Brian Moses

Mystery Visitor

"Who's whistling outside the door?
Who's there?" said Paul.
"It's just the wind in the trees, my boy,
Nothing to fear at all."

"Who's banging so hard on the door?
Who's there?" said Dad.
"It's just the thunder passing by,
Nothing dangerous or bad."

"What's that coming in through the door?
What can it be?" said Mum.
"It's a pile of letters," said Elizabeth-Jane.
"Oh good, the postman's come!"

David Orme

12

Blood and Bones

Under the floorboards, cold and deep,
Pipes are laid that drip and seep.
Down below the house, in the damp, dark mud,
Do they drip water or do they drip …?

Blood in my arteries!
Blood in my veins!
I dreamt that blood ran
down the drains!

High above the ceilings rafters creak.
Blind bats blunder. Mad mice squeak.
Up in the roof there are rattles and moans.
Is it the wind or chains and …?

Bones in my body!
Bones in my head!
I dreamt there was a skeleton
in my bed!

Celia Warren

13

Grandpa's Shed

When it's dark
Don't go near
Grandpa's shed

There are spiders
As big as a bed
In Grandpa's shed

There are hairy rats
And scary bats
In Grandpa's shed

There's a ghost
Who's lost his head
In Grandpa's shed

At the end of the day
Stay well away
From Grandpa's shed

And how do I know?
because I AM the ghost
in Grandpa's shed

Roger Stevens

I'd Rather Not Tell

Over the bridge
across the field
up the hill
and down the lane
there's a house in a garden
I visited once
And I'll never go there again.

A house in a garden,
A room in a house,
A box in a room
Where only the mice
Are awake when
– Now and again –
The lid gently opens,
All by itself,
And out comes – well?
No, I'd rather not tell.

Over the bridge
across the field
up the hill
and down the lane
there's a house in a garden
I visited once
And I'll never go there again.

David Orme

Davy Bones

Davy Bones lives in the wood
He rattles in the wind,
His ribs knock knock
Like a chopping block
And his eye-holes whistle and sing.

Davy Bones will get me
I know he lies in wait,
I hear his rusty laughter
In the hinges of the gate.
Davy Bones will catch me
His smile is sharp and thin
And every time I close my eyes
The darkness fills with him.

Davy Bones is coming
On the stones his footsteps ring
His ribs knock knock
Like a chopping block
And his eye-holes whistle and sing ...

Jan Dean

The Phantom Chain Rattler of No 53 Park Street

When midnight strikes
     and you're lying in bed
You'll hear the chains
     of Mister Dread!
I may be old
     and I may be dead
But I'll be there
     inside your head!

So …
Rattle rattle CLUNK!
     keep it spooky
Rattle rattle CLANK!
     Keep it fluky
I
won't
let you sleep
When I sneak through the keyhole
CREEP CREEP CREEP.

"There's no such thing as ghosts!"
        you said,
So why do you hide under
        your bedspread?
My hands are green
        my eyes are red
I live in a coffin
        and it's made of lead!

So …
Rattle rattle CLUNK!
        keep it spooky
Rattle rattle CLANK!
        Keep it fluky
I
won't
let you sleep
When I sneak through the keyhole
CREEP CREEP CREEP.

David Orme

I Wouldn't Go in There

A light at the window.
An old rocking chair.
They say there are ghosts.
I wouldn't go in there.

There's lots of creaking,
And cold in the air
Even in summer.
I wouldn't go in there.

My ball's in the garden.
I don't know where.
But they say there are ghosts
So I wouldn't go in there.

Jill Townsend

Someone in White

Someone in white
Is out at night,
Slides over the grass
Like glass,
Stops at the gate
To wait
Then hears a sound
And disappears.

Jill Townsend

Have You Ever?

Have you ever …
been on a ghost train,
where bats fly,
the shadows sigh
and darkness moans?

Have you ever …
heard on a ghost train,
click-clack wheels,
the skeleton squeals
and rattling bones?

Have you ever …
seen on a ghost train,
spiders dangle,
cobwebs tangle,
grey tombstones?

Have you ever …
felt on a ghost train
…
NO THANKS!

Judith Nicholls

The Ghostly Visitor

When the moon is out to play
And the shadows are deep
When the curtains are drawn
And everyone is asleep

There's a noise in the garden
A scrunching and scratching
There's a noise in the garden
A sniffling and snuffling

By the moon's ghostly light
In the shadows so deep
A breath flutters the curtains
And you can't get to sleep

There's a noise in the garden
But what can you do?
Is it a ghost?
Is the ghost after you?

The snuffling comes closer
The snuffling is here
You peer round the curtain
Your eyes wide with fear

Is the ghost of the garden
On its nightly patrol?
No – it's only a hedgehog
Out for a stroll

Roger Stevens

Hallowe'en

Midnight.
An owl hoots,
frost stiffens the air.
Tick …
    Tock …

The wind holds its breath,
no moon to be found.
Tick …
    Tock …
Tick …

Close eyes, block ears,
pull blankets tightly round.
Tick …
    Tock …
Tick …
    Tock …
Tick …

WHAT WAS THAT SOUND?

Judith Nicholls

Song of the Martian Ghosts

Mars was a beautiful planet once,
Just like yours –
Forests and mountains,
Seas crashing on rocky shores,
And us – the Martians.
But our seas dried up,
Our forests died,
We couldn't stay alive,
However hard we tried –
And now we're just ghosts,
Whispering in the cold wind,
In the dark places under rocks,
Waiting for you to arrive.

Come quickly, you men –
For when
Your first silver ship lands,
And opens its doors,
We'll slip inside,
For that's our plan –
To hitch a ride
To your beautiful green planet in the sky,
Where it's warm and wet,
And we can live again.

And once we're there
You'll never get rid of us.
However hard you try.

David Orme